teacher PLANNER

THIS PLANNER BELONGS TO:

_____

Want free goodies?!

Email us at

prettysimplebooks@gmail.com

Title the email "Teacher Planner!"
and let us know that you purchased
a Pretty Simple Planner!

Find us on Instagram!

@prettysimplebooks

Questions & Customer Service:
Email us at prettysimplebooks@gmail.com!

IMPORTANT DATES

January
NEW YEAR'S DAY
MARTIN LUTHER KING DAY

February
GROUNDHOG DAY
VALENTINE'S DAY
PRESIDENTS DAY

March
ST. PATRICK'S DAY

July
INDEPENDENCE DAY

August

September
LABOR DAY

April

APRIL FOOL'S DAY
EARTH DAY

May

CINCO DE MAYO
MOTHER'S DAY
MEMORIAL DAY

June

FATHER'S DAY

October

COLUMBUS DAY
HALLOWEEN

November

VETERANS DAY
THANKSGIVING

December

HANUKKAH
CHRISTMAS EVE
CHRISTMAS DAY
NEW YEAR'S EVE

July 2019

SUNDAY	MONDAY	TUESDAY	WEDNESDAY
	1	2	3
7	8	9	10
14	15	16	17 National Hot Dog Day
21 National Ice Cream Day	22	23	24
28	29	30	31

Live in the sunshine, swim in the sea, drink the wild air.
-Ralph Waldo Emerson

THURSDAY	FRIDAY	SATURDAY	NOTES
4 INDEPENDENCE DAY	5	6	_____ _____ _____ _____
11	12	13	_____ _____ _____ _____
18	19	20	_____ _____ _____ _____
25	26	27	_____ _____ _____ _____
			_____ _____ _____ _____

WEEK OF _____	Monday	Tuesday
SUBJECT:		

Wednesday	Thursday	Friday

WEEK OF _____	Monday	Tuesday
SUBJECT:		

Wednesday	Thursday	Friday

WEEK OF _____	Monday	Tuesday
SUBJECT:		

Wednesday	Thursday	Friday

WEEK OF _____	Monday	Tuesday
SUBJECT:		

Wednesday	Thursday	Friday

August 2019

SUNDAY	MONDAY	TUESDAY	WEDNESDAY
4	5	6 *Root Beer Float Day*	7
11	12	13	14
18	19	20	21
25	Bend #1 start Session #1 26	Session #2 27	Session #3 28

> The secret of getting ahead is getting started.
> — Mark Twain

THURSDAY	FRIDAY	SATURDAY	NOTES
1	2	3	*print out cluster #1 for binder
8	9	10	
15	16 Tell A Joke Day	17	small groups: focus on plot (3.8c) ↳ plot roller coaster chart
22 Read lucy lessons 1-4	23 spelling list goes home	24	
29 session #4	30 spelling test pre Assessment over ELAR essential 3.8c-plot catch-up day / assessment day	31	

WEEK OF 8/26	Monday	Tuesday
SUBJECT: Grammar	grammar patterns of power	
Writing	spelling patterns of power minilesson writing	
Reading		

Wednesday	Thursday	friday
		Assessment

WEEK OF _____	Monday	Tuesday
SUBJECT:		

Wednesday	Thursday	Friday

WEEK OF _____	Monday	Tuesday
SUBJECT:		

Wednesday	Thursday	Friday

WEEK OF _____	Monday	Tuesday
SUBJECT:		

Wednesday	Thursday	Friday

WEEK OF _____	Monday	Tuesday
SUBJECT:		

Wednesday	Thursday	Friday

September 2019

SUNDAY	MONDAY	TUESDAY	WEDNESDAY
1	no school 2 LABOR DAY	Session #5 3	Session #6 4
8	Session #8 9	Session # 9 10	Session #10 11
15	Session #12 16 1> teacher design (READING)	Session #13 17	Session #14 18 SUB
22	Session #16 23	24	25
29	30 ROSH HASHANAH		

With the new day comes new strength
and new thoughts.
                          – Eleanor Roosevelt

THURSDAY	FRIDAY	SATURDAY	NOTES
Session #7 **5**	assessment day **6** *Read a Book Day*	**7**	_____
Session #11 **12**	Aim for DRA done **13**	**14**	_____
Sesson #15 **19** modeled-morning Observed-afternoon	DRA'S due IN AWARE **20**	**21**	_____
26	Cluster #1 finished **27**	**28** *Good Neighbor Day*	_____
			_____

WEEK OF _____

SUBJECT:

Monday	Tuesday

Wednesday	Thursday	Friday

WEEK OF _____	Monday	Tuesday
SUBJECT:		

Wednesday	Thursday	Friday

WEEK OF _____	Monday	Tuesday
SUBJECT:		

Wednesday	Thursday	Friday

WEEK OF _____	Monday	Tuesday
SUBJECT:		

Wednesday	Thursday	Friday

October 2019

SUNDAY	MONDAY	TUESDAY	WEDNESDAY
	unit2 Session #1	1	2
6	unit 2 session #5 — 7	8	9 YOM KIPPUR
13	no school 14 COLUMBUS DAY	unit 2 Session 15 #9 running records due for below level	Session #10 16
20	unit 2 Session 21 #12	22	23
27	reading snapshot start! 28	session #16 29	Session #17 30

THURSDAY	FRIDAY	SATURDAY	NOTES
read frog+toad before thursday **3**	gms author visit field trip **4** *National Taco Day*	**5**	_____
10	staff (8-3:30) development **11** pre conference @3:45-4:15pm	**12**	_____
session #11 **17**	**18**	**19**	_____
24	**25**	**26**	_____
session #18/19 **31** HALLOWEEN	fun run event		_____

WEEK OF _____

SUBJECT:

	Monday	Tuesday

Wednesday	Thursday	Friday

WEEK OF _____	Monday	Tuesday
SUBJECT:		

Wednesday	Thursday	Friday

WEEK OF _____	Monday	Tuesday
SUBJECT:		

Wednesday	Thursday	Friday

WEEK OF _____

SUBJECT:

Monday

Tuesday

Wednesday	Thursday	Friday

WEEK OF _____

SUBJECT:

Monday

Tuesday

Wednesday	Thursday	Friday

November 2019

SUNDAY	MONDAY	TUESDAY	WEDNESDAY
3 DAYLIGHT SAVINGS ENDS	~~Mr Crackers~~ 4 mystery unit starts (3.8d)	5	6
10	11 VETERANS DAY	12 World Kindness Day	13
17	18	19	20
24	25	26	27

> The purpose of our lives is to be happy.
> — Dalai Lama

THURSDAY	FRIDAY	SATURDAY	NOTES
	reading snapshot due 1	2	_____
7	8	9	_____
14	15	16	_____
21	22	23	_____
28 THANKSGIVING	29	30	_____

WEEK OF _____

SUBJECT:

Monday

Tuesday

Wednesday	Thursday	Friday

WEEK OF _____	Monday	Tuesday
SUBJECT:		

Wednesday	Thursday	Friday

WEEK OF _____	Monday	Tuesday
SUBJECT:		

Wednesday	Thursday	Friday

WEEK OF _____	Monday	Tuesday
SUBJECT:		

Wednesday	Thursday	Friday

December 2019

SUNDAY	MONDAY	TUESDAY	WEDNESDAY
1	2	3	4
8	9	10	11
15	16	17	18
22	23 HANUKKAH	24 CHRISTMAS EVE	25 CHRISTMAS DAY
29	30	31 NEW YEAR'S EVE	

> What is done in love is done well.
>
> – Vincent Van Gogh

THURSDAY	FRIDAY	SATURDAY	NOTES
5	6	7	_____
12	13	14	_____
19	*last day before christmas break* 20	21	_____
26 KWANZAA	27	28	_____
			_____

WEEK OF _____	Monday	Tuesday
SUBJECT:		

Wednesday	Thursday	Friday

WEEK OF _____	Monday	Tuesday
SUBJECT:		

Wednesday	Thursday	Friday

WEEK OF _____	Monday	Tuesday
SUBJECT:		

Wednesday	Thursday	Friday

WEEK OF _____

SUBJECT:

Monday

Tuesday

Wednesday	Thursday	Friday

January 2020

SUNDAY	MONDAY	TUESDAY	WEDNESDAY
			1 NEW YEAR'S DAY
5	Staff development 6	back from christmas break 7 Research unit starts	8
12	13	14	15
19 National Popcorn Day	20 MARTIN LUTHER KING JR. DAY	21	22
26	27	28	29

> Nothing is impossible, the word itself
> says 'I'm possible'!
> — Audrey Hepburn

THURSDAY	FRIDAY	SATURDAY	NOTES
2	3	4	3.6G 3.9D(i)(ii)
9	10	11	
16	17	18	
23	24	25	
National Pie Day			
30	31		

WEEK OF _____	Monday	Tuesday
SUBJECT:		

Wednesday	Thursday	Friday

WEEK OF _____	Monday	Tuesday
SUBJECT:		

Wednesday	Thursday	Friday

WEEK OF _____	Monday	Tuesday
SUBJECT:		

Wednesday	Thursday	Friday

WEEK OF _____	Monday	Tuesday
SUBJECT:		

Wednesday	Thursday	Friday

WEEK OF _____	Monday	Tuesday
SUBJECT:		

Wednesday	Thursday	Friday

february 2020

SUNDAY	MONDAY	TUESDAY	WEDNESDAY
2	3	4	5
9	10 Character studies start	11 _Make a friend Day_	12
16	17 PRESIDENTS' DAY	18	19
23	24	25	26

> I have found if you love life, life will love you back.
> – Arthur Rubinstein

THURSDAY	FRIDAY	SATURDAY	NOTES
		1	3.8B 3.6f
6	7	8	
13	14 VALENTINE'S DAY	15	
20	21	22	
27	28	29	

WEEK OF _____	Monday	Tuesday
SUBJECT:		

Wednesday	Thursday	Friday

WEEK OF _____

SUBJECT:

Monday

Tuesday

Wednesday	Thursday	Friday

WEEK OF _____	Monday	Tuesday
SUBJECT:		

Wednesday	Thursday	Friday

WEEK OF _____	Monday	Tuesday
SUBJECT:		

Wednesday	Thursday	Friday

March 2020

SUNDAY	MONDAY	TUESDAY	WEDNESDAY
1	2	3	4
8 DAYLIGHT SAVINGS BEGINS	9	10	11
15	16	17 ST. PATRICK'S DAY	18
22	Poetry starts 23 3.6P 3.3B	24	25
29	30	31	

> Anything can happen if you let it.
> – Mary Poppins

THURSDAY	FRIDAY	SATURDAY	NOTES
5	6	7	3.6P
			3.3B
12	13	14 National Pi Day	
19	20	21	
26	27	28	

WEEK OF _____	Monday	Tuesday
SUBJECT:		

Wednesday	Thursday	Friday

WEEK OF _____

SUBJECT:

Monday

Tuesday

Wednesday	Thursday	Friday

WEEK OF _____	Monday	Tuesday
SUBJECT:		

Wednesday	Thursday	Friday

WEEK OF _____	Monday	Tuesday
SUBJECT:		

Wednesday	Thursday	Friday

April 2020

SUNDAY	MONDAY	TUESDAY	WEDNESDAY
			1
5	6	7	8
12 EASTER	13	14	15
19	*test prep* 20	21	22 EARTH DAY
26	27	28	29

THURSDAY	FRIDAY	SATURDAY	NOTES
2	3	4	
9	10 GOOD FRIDAY	11	
16	17	18	
23	24	25	
30			

WEEK OF _____	Monday	Tuesday
SUBJECT:		

Wednesday	Thursday	Friday

WEEK OF _____	Monday	Tuesday
SUBJECT:		

Wednesday	Thursday	Friday

WEEK OF _____	Monday	Tuesday
SUBJECT:		

Wednesday	Thursday	Friday

WEEK OF _____	Monday	Tuesday
SUBJECT:		

Wednesday	Thursday	Friday

May 2020

SUNDAY	MONDAY	TUESDAY	WEDNESDAY
3	4	5 *Cinco de Mayo*	6
10 MOTHER'S DAY	11	12 STAAR MATH	13 STAAR READING TEST
17	18	19	20
24 / 31	25 MEMORIAL DAY	26	27

THURSDAY	FRIDAY	SATURDAY	NOTES
	1	2	_____
7	8	9	_____
14	15	16	_____
21	22	23	_____
28	29	30 Water a Flower Day	_____

WEEK OF _____

SUBJECT:

Monday

Tuesday

Wednesday	Thursday	Friday

WEEK OF _____	Monday	Tuesday
SUBJECT:		

Wednesday	Thursday	Friday

WEEK OF _____	Monday	Tuesday
SUBJECT:		

Wednesday	Thursday	Friday

WEEK OF _____	Monday	Tuesday
SUBJECT:		

Wednesday	Thursday	Friday

June 2020

SUNDAY	MONDAY	TUESDAY	WEDNESDAY
	1	2	3
7	8	9	10
14 FLAG DAY	15	16	17
21 FATHER'S DAY	22	23	24
28	29	30	

[Adventure is worthwhile in itself.
- Amelia Earhart]

THURSDAY	FRIDAY	SATURDAY	NOTES
4	5	6	_____
	National Donut Day		_____
11	12	13	_____
18	19	20	_____
25	26	27	_____
			_____

WEEK OF _____	Monday	Tuesday
SUBJECT:		

Wednesday	Thursday	Friday

WEEK OF _____	Monday	Tuesday
SUBJECT:		

Wednesday	Thursday	Friday

WEEK OF _____	Monday	Tuesday
SUBJECT:		

Wednesday	Thursday	Friday

WEEK OF _____	Monday	Tuesday
SUBJECT:		

Wednesday	Thursday	Friday

WEEK OF _____	Monday	Tuesday
SUBJECT:		

Wednesday	Thursday	Friday

STUDENT BIRTHDAYS

January	February	March

July	August	September

April	May	June

October	November	December

Made in the USA
Lexington, KY
03 June 2019